KIT WILLIAMS

MASQUERADE

Within the pages of this book there is a story told
Of love, adventures, fortunes lost, and a jewel of solid gold.
To solve the hidden riddle, you must use your eyes,
And find the hare in every picture that may point you to the prize.

JONATHAN CAPE
THIRTY BEDFORD SQUARE LONDON

Once upon a perfect night, unclouded and still, there came the face of a pale and beautiful lady. The tresses of her hair reached out to make the constellations, and the dewy vapours of her gown fell soft upon the land.

Each picture in this book has a hare in it somewhere. Can you find him in this picture?

AS OLD AS EARTH

AND IN THE EARTH AM I

I AM AS COLD AS EARTH

ONE OF SIX TO EIGHT

This lady, whom all mortals call the Moon, danced a merry dance in the pathless sky, for she had fallen in love, and the object of her devotion was the Sun.

Although all happiness was in her dance, there was also a little sadness, for whenever the dance led her into the same part of the sky as the Sun, she seemed to simply fade away, and feared the Sun might never notice her.

The Sun, for his part, and contrary to his appearance, was always sad. The one thing he wished for most was a friend. But when people looked at him they immediately screwed up their faces and turned away, which made the Sun think that he must be terribly ugly.

On this night the lady of the pale complexion resolved to make herself known to the Sun by sending him a token of her affection.

To this end she asked the man that plays the music to stop playing for a while; then she plucked from the sea of clouds a most brilliant rose-coloured moonstone. Next, with a little gold taken from the dawn sky, she cunningly wrought a splendrous jewel that was the perfect mirror of her love. It had about it a beauty more permanent than the soft lip or flashing eye, a beauty that is for ever and mocks Time.

When the work was done and the stone was set, the pale and beautiful lady sent for her special messengers, the frog and the hare; the hare because he was as swift as the wind, and the frog for his wisdom, as old as the hills.

"Jack Hare," said she, "listen well. I entrust you with this amulet, and you have but one day to deliver it to my Lord the Sun. Take care, for the way of the little messenger is full of dangers, and yours especially so. Through earth and air and fire and water you must journey, until you reach my Lord the Sun. When you have reached him, show him the jewel and say to him it will be his if he will only give me the answer to this riddle:

> "Fifty is my first,
> Nothing is my second,
> Five just makes my third,
> My fourth a vowel is reckoned,
>
> "Now to find my name,
> Fit my parts together,
> I die if I get cold,
> But never fear cold weather.

"Now be off, Jack, and be quick! And you, frog, you must follow Jack's fortune and help him when you can. Although his legs, like yours, are long, his brain is very small and he may falter in this errand."

Jack set off with a great bound and a purposeful expression, pretending he knew exactly where to go and how to get there. But it wasn't long before he was most terribly lost and just jogged along muttering to himself,

"Jack, Jack do this, do that, it's always old Jack Hare, on the go from dusk to dawn, the Hare-bell's always ringing. Jack be quick and Jack in a box and Jack be in the cellar. Well ... Jack's as good as his mistress and Ja——— ... "

BUMP!

He was so caught up in his own little troubles that he hadn't noticed the Penny-Pockets Lady on the road, selling her fortunes.

"Where's your penny, Long Ears? A penny for your fortune."

"I've no penny," said Jack.

"No penny? No penny? Then why go bumping into people? Have you no manners?"

"No—er—yes, I mean—I just want to know which way to the Sun—er—please."

"If you've no penny then you must answer this riddle:

"I have a little house,
Its windows number plenty,
It's full of flowers that no man picked,
And you may have it when it's empty."

Jack answered directly, as it was so simple, and licked his lips and whiskers. "Now, which way to the Sun?"

The lady took her hand from her pocket and pointed UP.

Jack looked up and was astonished to see far above him a tiny figure moving from cloud to cloud. Just then, the being swooped down to hover a few inches above his head.

"Good morning, how did you do?" said Jack, remembering his manners but forgetting his grammar.

"Hello, my name's Tara. Tara Tree-tops. Tara's from the Latin you know, and this is my friend Craw. Isn't he handsome?"

"'Ansome, 'ansome, 'ansome," shrieked Craw, and puffed himself out to show off all his pretty feathers.

Nasty bird, thought Jack, but didn't say so.

"We were looking for lost dreams," said Tara, "they're all there up in the clouds, and when the clouds become too full they fall down again; the nasty ones as hailstorms with thunder, and the nice as gentle rain with rainbows. Most of them are quite boring though, like bishops' dreams of corduroy trousers, and bicycles for prime ministers. But sometimes I'm lucky enough to find the feasts of shipwrecked sailors or the palaces of chambermaids ... What's your dream?"

"I want to find the Sun," said Jack.

"Very well," said Tara, "but first you must hear my riddle:

"I have a little sister
And in the fields she's seen,
Dressed in yellow petticoats,
And a gown of green.
She's not a bird and cannot sing,
But she can fly without a wing.

"Now, jump with me and you may find the Sun behind a cloud."

The little hare jumped for all his worth, and up and up he went, over the tree tops, over the church steeple, and over the clouds—but the higher he got, the smaller the Sun became.

NOT AS HIGH

THE HILLS ARE

THE SEA SO DEEP

AS A DREAM

JACK HARE

IN HASTE TO CHASE

PETALS TUMB

As the hare got close to where the Sun *ought* to be, he heard the most terrible hullabaloo. All the people of earth had taken kettles and pans and sticks and pots, and drums and guns and gongs, and were making a fearful din; and this is the reason why.

The Lady Moon, disregarding all advice given to her by the other celestial bodies, had disobeyed Newton's Universal Law of Gravitation, and instead of continuing her dance in her prescribed orbit, had stayed behind to watch with anticipation the progress of the little hare. It was in thus doing that the unhappy Moon was the instrument of her own undoing. To understand completely, you need to solve this simple riddle:

> I am the beginning of eternity,
> Followed by half a circle, close on by half a square,
> Through my fourth my fifth is seen,
> To be the first in every pair.
> My sixth begins my seventh,
> The end of time and space,
> Now put my parts together to see what's taken place.

When the lady realised what she had done, and saw the hare falling out of the sky and all the other animals running in terror for their lives, she opened her mouth and SCREAMED. A horrible, silent, ghostly scream. The sort of scream that will turn the milk, sour the cream, blight a crop, and lame a horse as it stands in its stall.

All the horrors of the night came forth in this one dreadful scream.

The Sun was gone now and the fingers of shadowy night chilled the air. The shrieking and wailing of the people and the banging of their drums reached a climax. Cold panic gripped the animals, and those that only moments before were the deadliest of enemies ran side by side. The fox and the goose, the owl and the shrew, the cat and the hound ran round and round and round until they turned into one huge zoological pudding!

Even the animals themselves were unable to distinguish one from another … In fact, that's how the animals got their tails, but that's in another story. (See if you can count the animals in the picture opposite and give them all names. The answer is at the bottom of the page.)

Jack's small brain was ill-equipped to deal with such a commotion and it was as much as he could do to remember who he was. To save him from losing his wits entirely, he repeated to himself this, his own little riddle:

> "A hopper of ditches,
> A cropper of corn,
> A little brown deer,
> With leathery horn."

This went on until, little by little, the Sun returned and the people, realising that the demon of the night hadn't eaten their Sun after all, stopped the banging and shouting and went back to work.

After carefully disentangling himself from all the other animals, Jack ran off to hide in a tree, just in case it should all happen again.

There are twelve animals: a cat, a corse, a horse, a hog (saddle-back of course), a dog, a dow, a cow, a care, a hare, a ham, a ram and a rat.

Now that the eclipse had passed, Jack decided to continue his journey, but just then he heard the strains of a sad and sorrowful tune. Looking out of the tree in which he was hiding, he saw a curious little man sitting upon a hillock, playing a violin. Jack jumped down; the little man was the oldest, most crinkled creature he had ever seen, except for an aged tortoise in Dudley Zoo.

"Good day," said the musician. "I am the man that plays the music that makes the world go round. Can I help you?"

Jack related his story and the man stopped the music. "In my opinion," said he, "you require the assistance of the Practical Man. I am but a poet and a musician. You must go to the town and seek him out. To help you on your way, I shall play the Song of the Sun. The Sun is the eye of day, and as long as I play this tune, the day's eye cannot close again."

The man played the Song of the Sun so sweetly that it made the happy daisies grow, and with the sound of the song in his ears, Jack set off. But when he got to the town, all the shops were closed on account of it being Wednesday and half-day closing. However, there was one dingy little antique shop that stayed open, "so as to catch the passing trade". Jack peered in through the window.

"Step in," said the proprietor through the glass, "I have many treasures of antiquity that will take your fancy, or maybe I can show you an hare-loom or two?"

Oh dear, thought Jack, a humorist.

A ROSE IN MAY

RIDDLE DE DE

FIDDLE DE DE DE DUM

RIDDLE DE DE

A DAISY DAY

THE GREEN

EYE GLASS

ER TO PASS

Jack entered the shop.

"Excuse me, sir, are you the Practical Man?"

"Practical! On Wednesday afternoons I could be practically anything. What's up?"

Jack told of his adventures — about the jump, the Sun going out, and the little tortoise-like man. To listen better, the Practical Man took off his glasses and polished them with a red and white spotted handkerchief, but when it came to the bit about GOLD, he popped them on his nose.

"Right!" said he. "I have the solution. Fetch that eye-glass from the window whilst I collect the few other things we'll need."

Moments later, the Practical Man had collected everything in an old cane-back chair. Picking the whole lot up, he waddled out of the shop.

"Come, let us take a little stroll, then some tea, and maybe a little something ... to eat."

Jack followed and they went down the street, along the promenade, and down to the beach. The town was a well-known seaside resort. They walked along the sand until they came to a deserted spot where the man emptied the chair of its contents and flopped himself down in it. "This is just the spot for our experiment. Fetch driftwood and make a pile of it just here." Jack did as he was told.

Taking the magnifying glass, the Practical Man held it over the pile and a tiny sun appeared on one of the sticks, getting hotter and hotter, until, with a PUFF! it burst into flame.

"The Sun's arrived!" cried the Practical Man, pulling a toasting fork from inside his jacket. "Now, my little beauty, jump in." With the sting of the toasting fork in his rump, Jack jumped ...

AT HIGH TEA

FIRE BOIL KETTLE

WAVE QUENCH FIRE

AT HIGH TIDE

At this point, Sir Isaac Newton himself enters the story. By now he is very old and grey, and some of his less good theories have been disproved by the clever men of today, but despite all, his Universal Law of Gravitation still rules everywhere.

Although the Moon had disobeyed his laws, and would therefore have to forfeit the Hare-bell, it seemed unfair that the brave little hare should end up toasted by the Practical Man. Besides, although this may not be the happiest of stories, it is not a tragedy.

When he saw Jack Hare jump towards the fire, and the Practical Man brandishing the toasting fork, Sir Isaac grabbed the strings of gravitational force that bound Jack to his destiny and PULLED ———

Jack was deflected mid-leap, swerved sideways and fell SPLASH into the water. This now completed the Moon's curious instructions. He'd started in the earth, had gone up into the air with Tara Tree-tops, had passed through the fire of the Practical Man, and now here he was in the water.

Down and down he fell into the gloomy depths, until he could hardly see a paw in front of his face.

Then, through the murky waters, he saw a distant yellow light. This must surely be the Sun, thought Jack. To find out what he really saw, answer this slippery riddle:

> My first begins first, and I am myself my second. My next is the end of ends, followed by the beginning of hope.
> Now put me on one line, and you will find my name,
> I live my whole life out of doors, but never feel the rain.

JACK QUICK

AND JACK JUMPS

JACK BE NIMBLE

OVER THE FLAME

Jack could see now that it wasn't the Sun after all.
"Glood day," said the fish, sounding like someone
with a mouthful of cherries.

"Oh," said Jack, "I thought you were my Sun."

"How abslurd."

"No, no," said Jack, "the SUN," and drew a big circle in
the water.

"Then why have you come to the blottom of the ocean?"

Dear me, thought Jack, this is going to take all day. I'll
flatter him. "Please, oh fish, most worthy, noble and glorious
fish, please, fishy most high, can you direct me to the Sun?"

"You've blissed out educated," said the fish conceitedly,
"blut I will help you if you can blanswer this riddle:

"What is nothing on its outside,
And nothing on its inside,
Is lighter than a fleather,
But ten men cannot pick it up?"

Jack opened his mouth and out came a bubble! "Correct,"
said the fish. "Now flollow the frog. He will show you where
lives the Spirit of Water. She will tell you how to get to the
Sun."

Jack followed the frog and they swam until they came to a
sparkling lake, where a charming young lady swam back and
forth, measuring its length.

"Next time she passes," said the frog, "ask her."

Jack did, and this was her strange reply:

"Stand at the water's edge a little before the Sun sets in the
west, and you will see a yellow carpet. If you can run its
length before the Sun has time to set, you will reach your
destination. Good luck!"

CRYSTAL

Already the golden light of late afternoon was colouring the sky, and Jack realised that time was getting short. So, running as fast as his legs would carry him, he set off for the West Country. With not a minute to spare, he reached the shore, and there, spread out over the sea between him and the Sun, was a bright yellow pathway. Without stopping, not even to take breath, the hare LEAPED.

Jack travelled so speedily and reached such a velocity that Sir Isaac Newton and his gravity were forced to let him go. He had now escaped the earth's powerful attraction, and was travelling end over end, through space towards the Sun.

Sir Isaac looked out over the sea and said to himself, "All my life I seem to have been only like a boy playing on the sea-shore and diverting myself in now and then finding a smoother pebble or a prettier shell than ordinary, whilst the great ocean of truth lay all undiscovered before me."

On reaching the Sun, Jack was horrified to find that he no longer had the jewel … IT WAS GONE!

"Well," said the Sun, with a loud commanding voice, "why have you come here?"

Jack thought quickly, then said, "Great Lord Sun, I bring you a precious gift from a noble and gracious lady, and it would be yours if it were not the answer to this riddle:

> "Fifty is my first,
> Nothing is my second,
> A snake will make my third,
> Then three parts a cross is reckoned.
> Now to find my name, fit my parts together,
> I am all your past, and you fear me in cold weather?"

THE SUN SET AND THE DAY WAS OVER.

Dear Reader,

If you were to read this book again, you might discover when and where the hare lost the jewel. If you do, then go and find it, and keep it for yourself, but remember:

The best of men is only a man at best,
And a hare, as everyone knows, is only a hare.

First published 1979
Reprinted 1979 (*three times*), 1980
© 1979 by Kit Williams
Jonathan Cape Ltd, 30 Bedford Square, London WC1

British Library Cataloguing in Publication Data
Williams, Kit
Masquerade.
I. Title
823'.9' IJ   PZ7.W/
ISBN 0 224 01617 2

Kit Williams's original works of art are exhibited
exclusively by Portal Gallery Ltd., London,
England.

Printed in Italy by A. Mondadori Editore, Verona